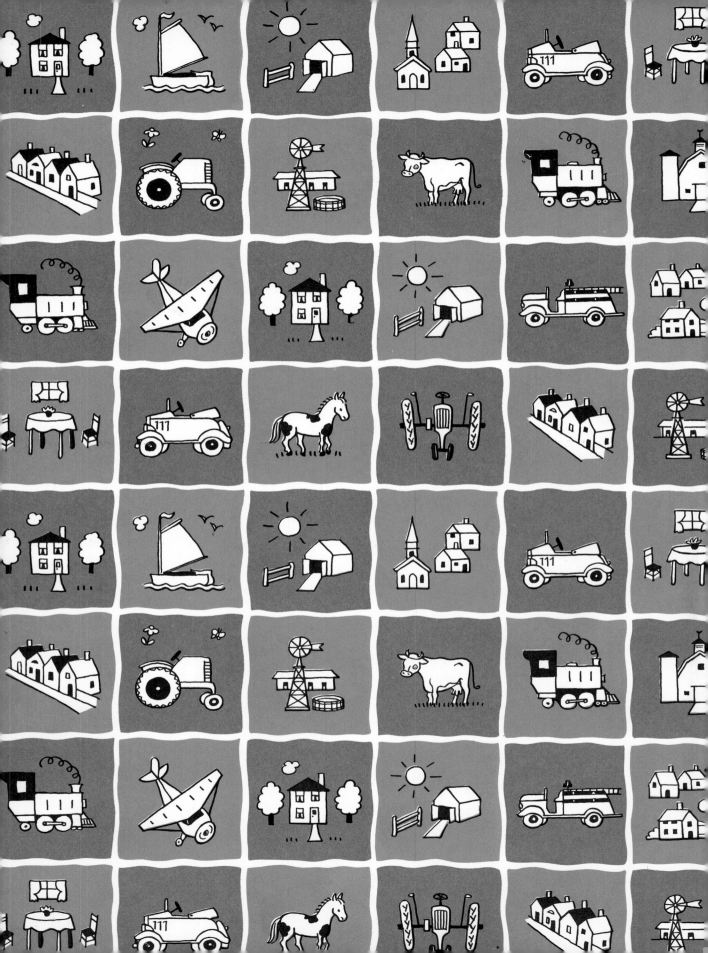

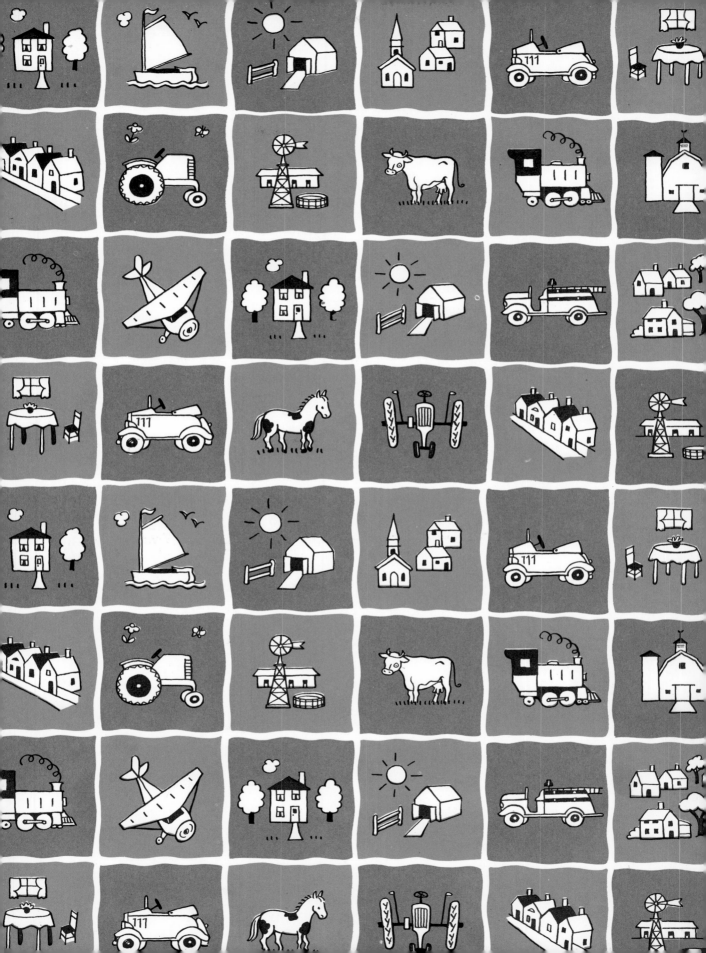

SONGS of MR. SMALL

SONGS
of MR. SMALL

Words and Pictures
by LOIS LENSKI

With Music

by CLYDE ROBERT BULLA

OXFORD UNIVERSITY PRESS
New York

1954

*To all the thousands of children
who have known and loved Mr. Small.*

Library of Congress Card Number 54-11903

CONTENTS

Foreword

A second generation of children is growing up who love Mr. Small in his various roles. Only the child himself understands the close bond he feels for this beloved book character, and the child is too inarticulate to explain. But the bond is there and a very real one.

Mr. Small takes on stature as the years go by. He is ever new and completely satisfying to the three-year-old who meets him for the first time. He soon becomes an indispensable part of his daily life. His charm does not fade and he continues to satisfy as the child grows older. Boys of ten and twelve, who have long outgrown him, like to chuckle as they leaf through the books. Always the reader identifies himself with Mr. Small and does all the things he does.

In the Mr. Small songs, his simple actions can be more vividly dramatized. The child does not just sing about Mr. Small. He is Mr. Small. When he sings, Mr. Small is singing. The songs will help, even more than the heard or spoken word, to bring Mr. Small alive. The child as Mr. Small makes the auto go, sails the sailboat, trots on the pony, plays with Tinker, rides the airplane and looks up at it from the ground. These are basic childhood experiences, common to every child. In the songs Mr. Small speaks for himself. May they help to increase the dramatic use of the books.

We, author and composer, deplore the increasing popularity of "popular" songs for children, common over radio and television; songs which are unchildlike in subject matter and appeal, and music which is a sophisticated adult expression. We are trying to offset this trend by offering simple songs that are basically childlike, wholesome and universal in appeal.

Mr. Small has been greatly loved by one generation of children, not only American but children of foreign lands. Now the children of those children love him dearly too. To them we give our songs. They were written with joy and spontaneity, with love and devotion, and always with the child in mind. May children everywhere read and sing about Mr. Small. May he truly become a part of their lives.

December 29, 1953
Tarpon Springs, Florida   *Lois Lenski*

January 4, 1954
Los Angeles, California   *Clyde Robert Bulla*

SONGS *of* MR. SMALL

Big Mr. Small

Words by LOIS LENSKI
Music by CLYDE ROBERT BULLA

1. Big Mis-ter Small Has an au-to red, He likes to go to town. He buys a pa-per, Gets some gas, He drives up hill and down.

2. Big Mis-ter Small Is an en-gin-eer, He drives an en-gine black. A coal car too, And coach-es new For peo-ple in the back.

3. Big Mis-ter Small Has a trac-tor green Out on his coun-try farm. He plows and plants And hauls his crops, He stores them in the barn.

4.   Big Mister Small
           Has a sailboat neat
For sailing on the lake.
           He'll eat his lunch,
           He'll catch a fish,
And then a swim he'll take.

5.   Big Mister Small
           Has an airplane too,
He flies up very high.
           He banks and turns,
           He loops a loop
'Way up there in the sky.

6.   Big Mister Small
           Is a fireman brave,
A pumper red he drives.
           He goes to fires
           And puts them out,
He saves the people's lives.

7.   Big Mister Small
           Is a cowboy now,
He rides the range all day.
           He breaks a bronc
           And if he falls,
Jumps on again to stay.

8.   Big Mister Small
           Is Papa too,
For he has children three.
           He helps his wife
           Around the house,
He's nice as he can be.

Ride a Red Auto

Words by LOIS LENSKI
Music by CLYDE ROBERT BULLA

1. Ride a red au-to to town, Mis-ter Small, Ride your car
2. Keep to the right side in town, Mis-ter Small, Keep to the
3. Ride a red au-to in town, Mis-ter Small, Park your car

up hill and down. All you ducks and chick-ens Get
right on the street. When the light turns green, Mis-ter
right by the store. Go and buy some gas, Get a

10

out of the way, Mis - ter Small is go - ing To town to - day.
Small, go a - head, But be sure to stop when The light turns red.
news - pa - per, then – Mis - ter Small is go - ing Back home a - gain.

NEWSPAPERS

PARK HERE

The Gas Station Man

Words by LOIS LENSKI
Music by CLYDE ROBERT BULLA

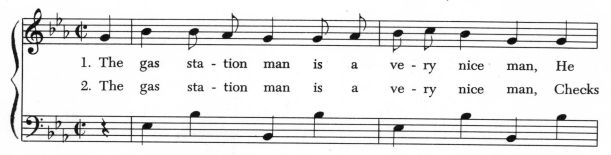

1. The gas sta-tion man is a ve-ry nice man, He
2. The gas sta-tion man is a ve-ry nice man, Checks

sells me all my gas, He waves and calls out, "Hi, Mis-ter Small!" Each
oil and wa-ter too, He cleans my wind-shield, Shines it __ bright, And

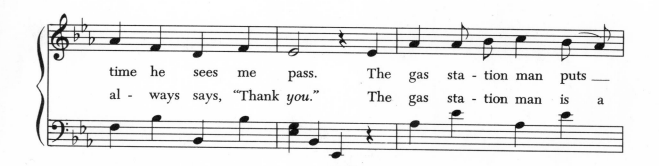

time he sees me pass. The gas sta-tion man puts __
al-ways says, "Thank *you*." The gas sta-tion man is a

gas in my tank, And then the bell it rings, He
friend of ___ mine In sum - mer, win - ter, fall, He

takes the mon - ey I hand out And then my change he brings.
chang - es tires and puts in air And calls me Mis - ter Small!

The Little Train

Words by LOIS LENSKI
Music by CLYDE ROBERT BULLA

1. The lit-tle train rides on the track, It goes to town and
2. In-side the coach the peo-ple ride, They're sit-ting down there
3. The train's on time, don't ev-er fear, For Mis-ter Small is

then comes back. It car-ries mail and trunks so new, It takes ex-press and
side by side. The en-gine's big and shin-y black, And up in front a
en-gin-eer. He rides in-side the cab so proud, He toots the whis-tle

14

bag-gage, too.   Choo, choo! Choo, choo, choo!   Choo, choo! Choo, choo, choo!

big smoke-stack.   Choo, choo! Choo, choo, choo!   Choo, choo! Choo, choo, choo!

long and loud—   Toot, toot! Toot, toot, toot!   Toot, toot! Toot, toot, toot!

4. The train must stop sometimes and then
 It whistles loud and goes again.
 The little train rides on the track,
 It goes to town and then comes back.
     Choo, choo!
     Choo, choo, choo!
     Choo, choo!
     Choo, choo, choo!

15

Out in the Country

Words by LOIS LENSKI
Music by CLYDE ROBERT BULLA

1. Out in the coun - try so qui - et, still, A whis - tle
2. Right down the track ___ the en - gine comes, Out leans the
3. Out in the field ___ the hors - es jump, They run and

loud ___ is heard; ___ A - bove the sound ___ of
en - gin - eer; ___ He waves his hand ___ and
frisk ___ and neigh; ___ The cows they nev - er

blow - ing breeze, A - bove the song _ of bird. _____
calls hel - lo To boy on fence _ so near. _____
move at all, They chew their cud _ all day. _____

4. Past all the houses and barns and trees,
   And over bridges high;
   The train chugs on and leaves a trail
   Of smoke up in the sky.

5. Out in the country so quiet, still,
   The whistle dies away;
   The gentle breeze begins to blow,
   And birds sing all the day.

If I Had a Tractor

Words by LOIS LENSKI
Music by CLYDE ROBERT BULLA

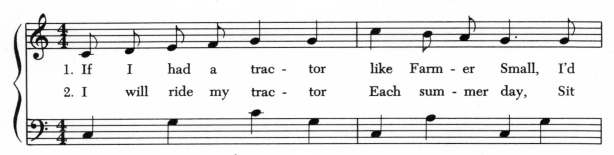

1. If I had a trac - tor like Farm - er Small, I'd
2. I will ride my trac - tor Each sum - mer day, Sit

ride round my farm From spring un - til fall. If I had a trac - tor
un - der my sun-shade And cut all my hay. I will ride my trac - tor

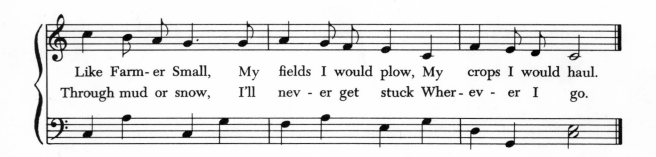

Like Farm - er Small, My fields I would plow, My crops I would haul.
Through mud or snow, I'll nev - er get stuck Wher - ev - er I go.

I Like to Live on the Farm

Words by LOIS LENSKI
Music by CLYDE ROBERT BULLA

1. I like to live on the farm ___ And get up with the sun! ___ I like to whis-tle and help make hay, And work till day is done. ___ (Whistle) _____

2. I like to milk ___ the cow ___ If she will just stand still; ___ I sing and whis-tle and tug and pull, And get the buc - ket full. ___ (Whistle) _____

3. I like to do ___ the chores ___ And drive the trac - tor too; ___ I like to live on the farm, ___ You can bet your life I do! ___ (Whistle) _____

My Roadside Stand

Words by LOIS LENSKI
Music by CLYDE ROBERT BULLA

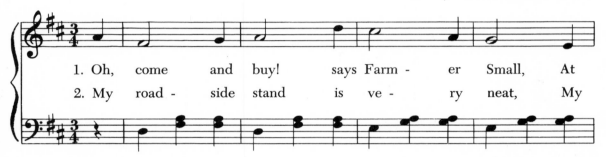

1. Oh, come and buy! says Farm - er Small, At
2. My road - side stand is ve - ry neat, My

road - side stand in ear - ly fall; Slow up and stop, See
ap - ples they are red and sweet; My beets and beans, And

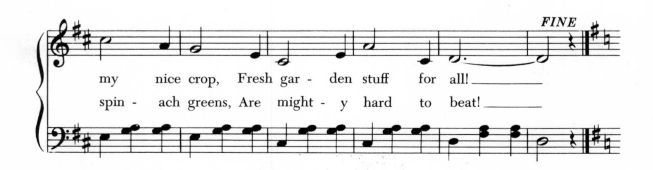

FINE

my nice crop, Fresh gar - den stuff for all! _____
spin - ach greens, Are might - y hard to beat! _____

Ap - ples in a bas - ket, Ci - der in a jug; Car - rots in

bunch - es, Pump - kins to lug. Bush beans by the bush - el,

D.C.

Let - tuce by the head; Eggs by the doz - en, And beets, big and red.

A Customer

A DIALOGUE SONG

Words by LOIS LENSKI
Music by CLYDE ROBERT BULLA

Mrs. Jones:

1. Good morn-ing, Farm-er Small! And how are you to-day? I
2. I'll take two pounds of beans, A head of let-tuce nice; A
3. No, thank you, Farm-er Small! That's all I need to-day, Good-

drove out from the ci-ty To buy some things to-day.
doz-en eggs, some spin-ach, Yours is the low-est price.
by and here's my mon-ey, I won't for-get to pay.

22

Farmer Small:

1. Good morn-ing, Mis - sus Jones! What can I get for you? I
2. And don't you want some beets? A pump - kin big and fat? A
3. Oh, thank you, Mis - sus Jones! I'll say good - by and then — A

have some beans and car - rots, Some beets and spin - ach too.
bas - ket of nice ap - ples— Now would-n't you like that?
safe drive to the ci - ty, And come out soon a - gain.

If I Had a Boat

Words by LOIS LENSKI
Music by CLYDE ROBERT BULLA

1. If I had a lit-tle boat, And it had mast and sail, I'd
2. If I had a great big boat, I'd sail it on the lake; I'd

put it in the wa-ter, In bath tub or in pail.
be her stur-dy cap-tain, A voy-age long I'd take.

If I had a big-ger boat, And it would real-ly go, I'd
If I could be Cap-tain Small, I'd take my lunch and then I'd

put it in the riv-er Where all the strong winds blow.
sail a-cross the o-cean And sail right back a-gain.

Over the Sea Sails He

Words by LOIS LENSKI
Music by CLYDE ROBERT BULLA

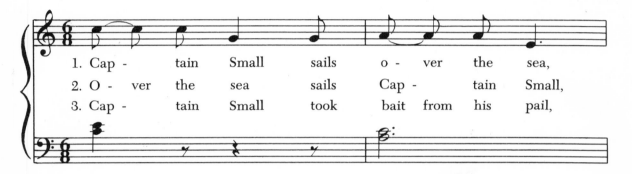

1. Cap - tain Small sails o - ver the sea,
2. O - ver the sea sails Cap - tain Small,
3. Cap - tain Small took bait from his pail,

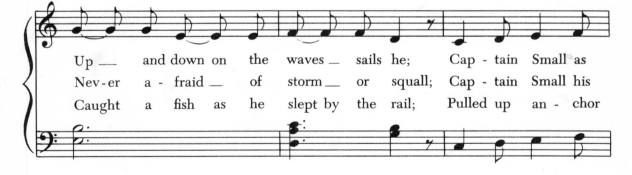

Up __ and down on the waves __ sails he; Cap - tain Small as
Nev - er a - fraid __ of storm __ or squall; Cap - tain Small his
Caught a fish as he slept by the rail; Pulled up an - chor

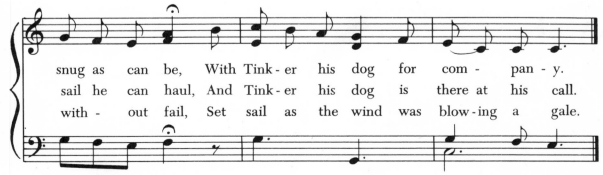

snug as can be, With Tink - er his dog for com - pan - y.
sail he can haul, And Tink - er his dog is there at his call.
with - out fail, Set sail as the wind was blow - ing a gale.

4th Verse: Repeat Verse 1.

25

The Bird With Silver Wings

Words by LOIS LENSKI
Music by CLYDE ROBERT BULLA

1. Up in the sky a big bird flies, A bird with sil - ver
2. Down on the ground a boy looks up, He sees the shin - ing
3. Up in the sky the clouds float by, While birds pass o - ver

wings; The sun shines bright and makes them shine, But the
bird; He waves and calls to Pi - lot Small, But his
head; The pi - lot's day is end - ing now, And the

bird it nev - er sings. Up in the sky a
words can - not be heard. Down from the sky the
sun is set - ting red. Down on the ground the

26

man looks down On roads and towns be - low; He
big bird comes, It lands and turns a - round; The
big bird rests, A man the lad - der brings; And

rides the bird with sil - ver wings, And makes the eng - ine go.
pi - lot o - pens up the door, He steps out on the ground.
Pi - lot Small looks back to see The bird with sil - ver wings.

Airplane, Airplane

Words by LOIS LENSKI
Music by CLYDE ROBERT BULLA

up to the sun that shines so bright. Air - plane,
straight — on up to touch the sky. Air - plane,

air - plane, Up in the sky, _____ Pi - lot
air - plane, Up in the sky, _____ Pi - lot

Small, Do you like to fly? _____
Small, Do you like to fly? _____

Fire Truck

Words by LOIS LENSKI
Music by CLYDE ROBERT BULLA

1. Clang, clang! The fire truck comes Down the street so fast.
2. Clang, clang! Where's the fire? See the smoke so black.

Clang, clang! Where's the fire? See it go - ing past!
Clang, clang! False a - larm — Now it's go - ing back!

30

Fireman Brave

Words by LOIS LENSKI
Music by CLYDE ROBERT BULLA

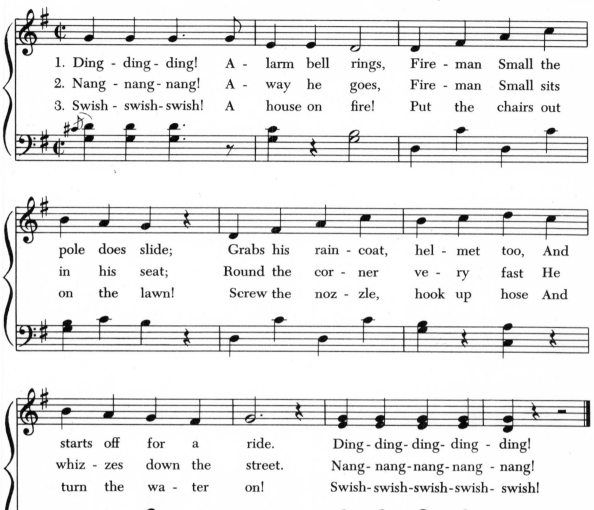

1. Ding - ding - ding! A - larm bell rings, Fire - man Small the
2. Nang - nang - nang! A - way he goes, Fire - man Small sits
3. Swish - swish - swish! A house on fire! Put the chairs out

pole does slide; Grabs his rain - coat, hel - met too, And
in his seat; Round the cor - ner ve - ry fast He
on the lawn! Screw the noz - zle, hook up hose And

starts off for a ride. Ding - ding - ding - ding - ding!
whiz - zes down the street. Nang - nang - nang - nang - nang!
turn the wa - ter on! Swish - swish - swish - swish - swish!

4.
Sizz-sizz-sizz!
He squirts the hose
At the flames and smoke so black.
Fireman Small puts out the fire
And then goes driving back.
Sizz-sizz-sizz-sizz-sizz!

Cactus—Mr. Small's Pony

Words by LOIS LENSKI
Music by CLYDE ROBERT BULLA

1. I have a lit - tle po - ny, And Cac - tus is his name, _ I brush him clean and feed him, For he is ve - ry tame. _ I'll take a ride on Cac - tus, I'll put the sad - dle on, _ I'll

2. I'll climb up on my po - ny, In stir - rups put my feet, _ I'll hold the reins so light - ly, Sit straight up in my seat. _ I'll say Gid - dap to Cac - tus, My po - ny he will trot _ Or

3. Gid - dap, let's go, Old Cac - tus! My po - ny white and brown, _ We'll ride a - round the pas - ture Be - fore the sun goes down. _ Let's turn a - round, Old Cac - tus, We'll ride right back and then _ I'll

pull the girth so tight - ly, And soon we will be gone. ___
walk or pace or gal - lop, Al - though the day is hot. ___
bed you down and feed you, And we'll be home a - gain. ___

Clop - pet - y, clop - pet - y, clop, clop. Clop - pet - y, clop - pet - y, clop.

Just Like a Cowboy

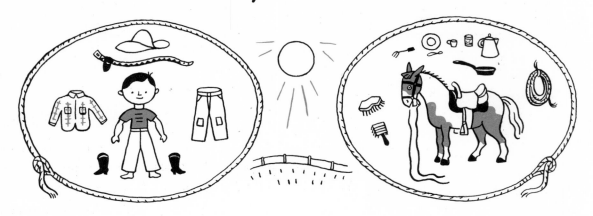

Words by LOIS LENSKI
Music by CLYDE ROBERT BULLA

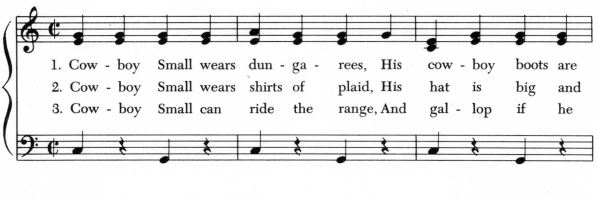

1. Cow - boy Small wears dun - ga - rees, His cow - boy boots are
2. Cow - boy Small wears shirts of plaid, His hat is big and
3. Cow - boy Small can ride the range, And gal - lop if he

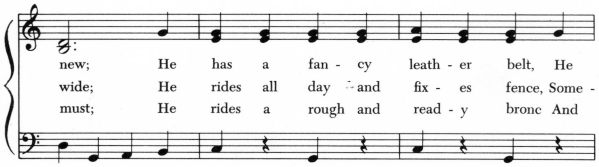

new; He has a fan - cy leath - er belt, He
wide; He rides all day and fix - es fence, Some -
must; He rides a rough and read - y bronc And

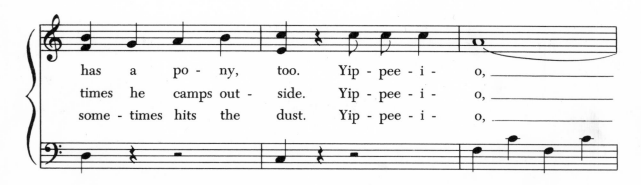

has a po - ny, too. Yip - pee - i - o, _____
times he camps out - side. Yip - pee - i - o, _____
some - times hits the dust. Yip - pee - i - o, _____

34

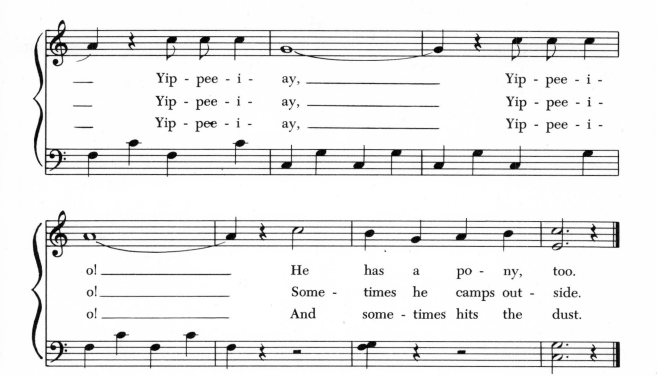

Yip - pee - i - ay, _____ Yip - pee - i -
Yip - pee - i - ay, _____ Yip - pee - i -
Yip - pee - i - ay, _____ Yip - pee - i -

o! _____ He has a po - ny, too.
o! _____ Some - times he camps out - side.
o! _____ And some - times hits the dust.

4. Cowboy Small sleeps in his bunk
   So soundly all night long;
   Sometimes he strums his old guitar
   And sings a cowboy song.
   Yip-pee-i-o, Yip-pee-i-ay, Yip-pee-i-o!
   And sings a cowboy song.

5. Cowboy Small can rope a cow
   And round up all the herd;
   He whoops and hollers very loud
   Just like a cowboy should.
   Yip-pee-i-o, Yip-pee-i-ay, Yip-pee-i-o!
   Just like a cowboy should.

Tinker—Mr. Small's Dog

Words by LOIS LENSKI
Music by CLYDE ROBERT BULLA

1. Tink - er likes to jump up, Tink - er likes to play;
2. Tink - er likes to lis - ten, Tink - er likes to growl;
3. Tink - er likes his mas - ter, Fol - lows Mis - ter Small;

Tink - er likes to sniff and smell, He's hun - gry all the day.
Tink - er likes to bark and bark, And some - times he will howl.
Tink - er likes to go for walks, And try to catch a ball.

Sniff sniff sniff, Bow wow wow, Sniff sniff sniff!
Wow wow wow, Girr girr girr, Wow wow wow!
Yap yap yap, Bow wow wow, Yap yap yap!

4. Tinker likes his auto,
   Tinker likes his boat;
   Tinker likes to take a ride
   On land or else afloat.
   Woof woof woof,
   Sniff sniff sniff,
   Woof woof woof!

Mama Small

Words by LOIS LENSKI
Music by CLYDE ROBERT BULLA

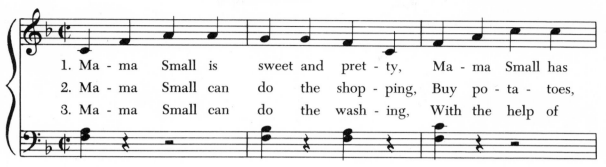

1. Ma - ma Small is sweet and pret - ty, Ma - ma Small has
2. Ma - ma Small can do the shop - ping, Buy po - ta - toes,
3. Ma - ma Small can do the wash - ing, With the help of

chil - dren three; Ma - ma Small can rock the ba - by,
bread and meat; Ma - ma Small can cook the din - ner,
Pa - pa Small; Ma - ma irons a dress for Pol - ly,

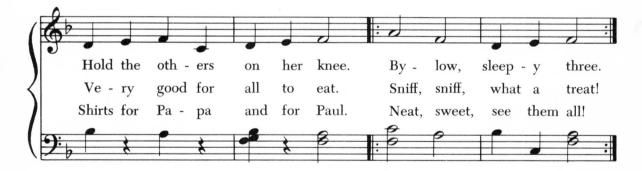

Hold the oth - ers on her knee. By - low, sleep - y three.
Ve - ry good for all to eat. Sniff, sniff, what a treat!
Shirts for Pa - pa and for Paul. Neat, sweet, see them all!

4. Mama Small can do the cleaning,
Sweep the house and dust it, too;
Paul and Polly like to help her,
Always happy when they do.
Swish, swish, yes, that's true!

What Do You Do, Papa Small?

A DIALOGUE SONG

Words by LOIS LENSKI
Music by CLYDE ROBERT BULLA

1. Q. Oh, What do you do at home, Pa - pa Small? At
2. Q. What else do you do at home, Pa - pa Small? What
3. Q. What else do you do at home, Pa - pa Small? What

night when you first come home? A. I run to meet my
work do you do at home? A. I fix the plumb - ing
else do you do at home? A. I plant the gar - den,

chil - dren sweet, And then we all sit down to eat.
nice and fine, I hang the clothes up on the line.
cut the grass And call hel - lo to all who pass.

4. Q. Where does your family go, Papa Small?
      On Saturday for a change?
   A. I take the family to the store,
      I buy some food and buy some more.

5. Q. Where do they go dressed up, Papa Small?
      On Sunday dressed so fine?
   A. We go to church, then in the car
      We take a ride both near and far.

6. Q. Is that all you do at home, Papa Small?
      Is that all you do at home?
   A. I read the paper and when it's read—
      Why, then it's time to go to bed!

That's All About Mr. Small

Words by LOIS LENSKI
Music by CLYDE ROBERT BULLA

1. I like to sing a-bout Mis-ter Small And all that he can do; I
2. I like to sing a-bout Mis-ter Small, His trac-tor, po-ny too; I

like his train, his big air-plane, I like his au-to too. And
like his sail-boat and his dog, I like his fire-truck new. And

now that's all a-bout Mis-ter Small, That's all a-bout Mis-ter Small.
now that's all a-bout Mis-ter Small, That's all a-bout Mis-ter Small.

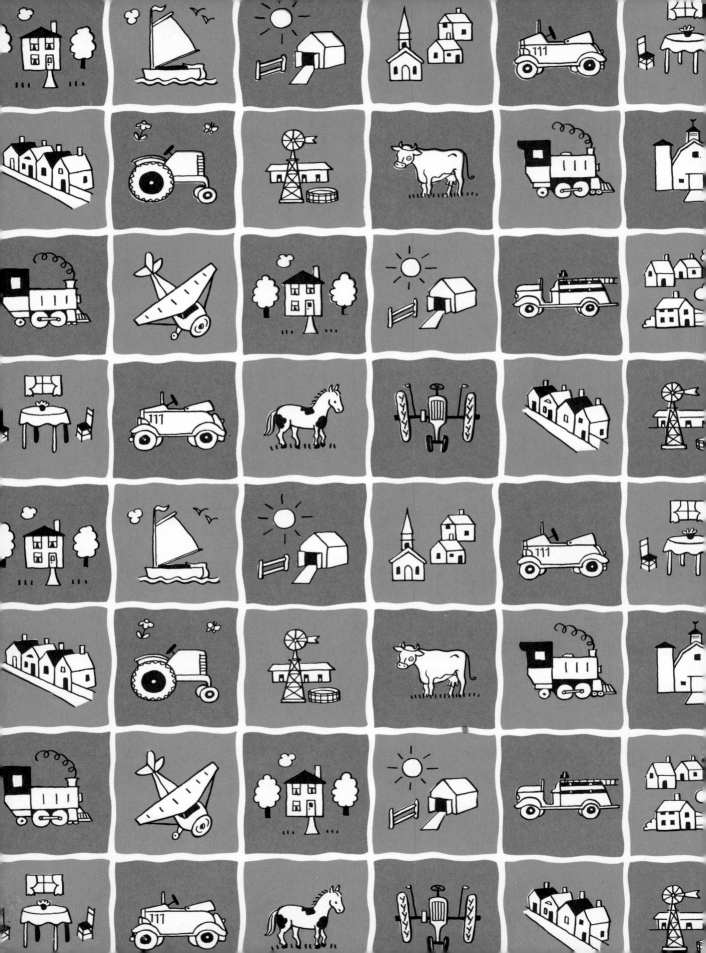

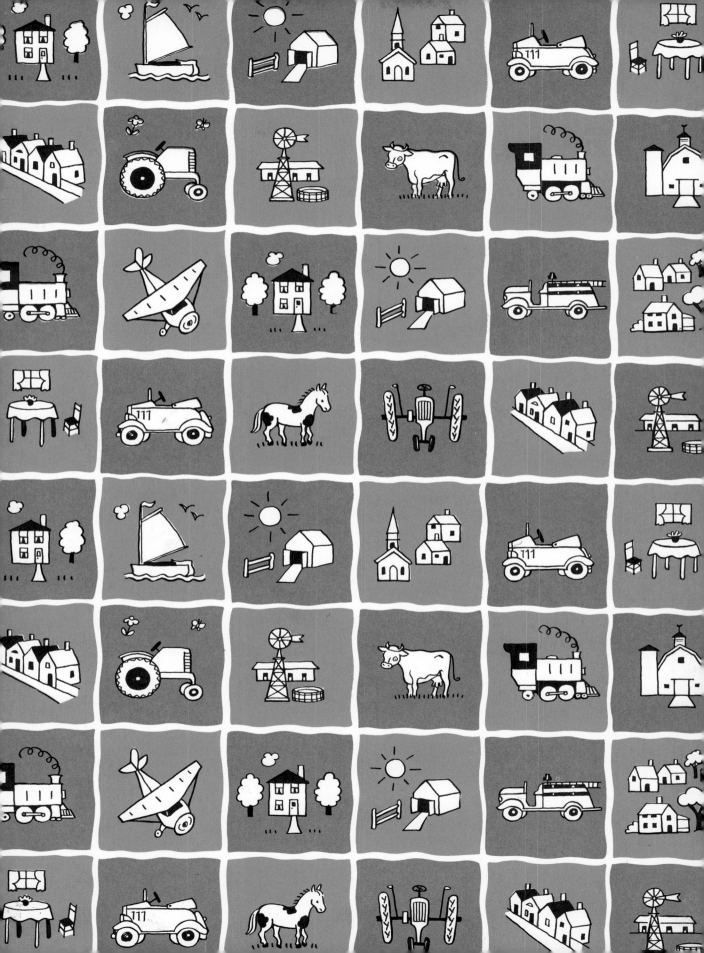